I CHOOSE YOU!

A collection of creatures by LISA JONES
and rhymes by JOANNA SKIPWITH

SILVER JUNGLE

I'm a whale, with a tail,
And I tell you it's smashing.
My bath is an ocean,
My homework
Is *splashing*!

It's cool to be green,
I should know, I'm a frog,
And I like to lie low
In a cool squelchy bog.
And I like to swim free
In my green weedy pool,
Down by the water reeds...

...totally cool.

I tiptoe up a tulip,
It takes me quite a while.
I pace myself and stop for snacks,
I like to crawl in style.
The view is good of the neighbourhood
If I climb a little higher,
And at the top, I double-check
That my house is *not* on fire.

My tail is ringed,
My eyes are patched,

My mischief and my smile
Unmatched!

I’m a butterfly, I flutter by
And as I fly I mutter,
But softly, so you may not hear
A smallish ‘hi’ or faint ‘goodbye’,
Not even when I flutter by
Right beside your ear.

If I could see ahead of me,
Of course I'd head *elsewhere*,
And dig towards your neighbour's lawn
To make a molehill there.

Oh deary me,
That's very weird,
My brand new bathroom's
Disappeared!

I am an owl
Beneath a cloud.
At night I like to sing out loud.
And as the song gets rowdier,
The evening sky grows cloudier.

I'm pampered and prettified,
Powdered and trimmed,
Dressed like a princess
In ribbons and bows.
You probably think
That I'm happy in pink,
But I'd love to wear *black*
And bite people's toes.

Do I look like a pineapple?
Apart from my feet?
Oh good. You see,
I'm camouflaged
And expecting to meet
An unsuspecting...

...SNAIL to eat!

PET SHOP

I bought a *something* from the shop,
They put it in a box.
It ate my gloves and then my hat,
And then it ate my socks.
I tried to make it spit them out,
I offered it some ham,
But it just scowled, as if to say,
'Who do you think I am?'

Apples keep me busy,
But I wish they weren't so *round*,
As I feel a little dizzy
When they roll along the ground.

I'm a collie without a collar,
Whiskers or a grin,
And I wish I had a name tag,
Just below a chin.
I wouldn't mind some sheep,
Or a shepherd with a crook,
But this is how a Rough Collie
Is roughly meant to look.

I'm very attached to my shell,
It's stylish, I think you'll agree,
Low energy, purpose-built,
And semi-attached to me!

Of all the creatures in this book,
Some mischievous, some shy,
I wonder if you'd choose to be
A mole, or butterfly?
The little whale, or giant snail?
I know that I'd choose *you*,
Because I see, immediately,
That you're a monkey, too!

Would you choose the monkey, or the cool frog?
The raccoon perhaps? Of all these creatures, the
monkey is the most similar to you: your wild cousin.

Many species are critically endangered, among
them: Brown Spider Monkeys in Columbia, Squirrel
Monkeys in Costa Rica, White-Naped Mangabeys in
Ghana and the Yellow-Tailed Woolly Monkeys of Peru.

I CHOOSE YOU! is supporting CERCOPAN
and helping to protect monkeys in the rainforests
of south-eastern Nigeria. Other Silver Jungle books
are raising money for tigers, rhinos and a tiny
hummingbird in Colombia. Please visit our website
to find out more.

www.silverjungle.com

Published by Silver Jungle Ltd
P.O. Box 51793, London NW1W 9AZ
www.silverjungle.com

First edition 2009, second impression 2010

Designed by Lisa Jones Studio
www.lisajonesstudio.com
Printed in England by Connekt Colour
on Splendorgel.

ISBN 978-0-9552652-3-5

Mixed Sources
Product group from well-managed
forests and other controlled sources
www.fsc.org Cert no. TT-COC-002679
© 1996 Forest Stewardship Council